The Kathy and Mark Bas

Indoors and Out

by MABEL O'DONNELL *and* RONA MUNRO

illustrated by Beatrice Darwin

NISBET

© 1966, 1970 Harper and Row   0 7202 1001 1

Mark, Mark.
It is on.

Come in, Mark.
Come in here.
The television is on.
Come and look.

3

Here I come, Kathy.
I like television.
I can see the cowboys.
Here come the cowboys.
I see two cowboys.

No, Mark, no.
I see three cowboys.
One, two, three.
Look, look.
Here come the Indians.
See the Indians, Mark.

Ride, cowboys, ride.
Here come the Indians.
Kathy, see the cowboys go.
See the Indians ride.
I like the Indians.
I like the cowboys.

The Ducks

Come on, Mother.
Come down here.
Come and look.

Look down here, Mother.
See the ducks.
See the little ducks.

I see the little ducks.
Kathy, look here.
Here is the mother duck.
Come and look.
One mother duck.
Three little ducks.

Mother, look.
The mother duck can swim.
Two little ducks go in.
Two little ducks can swim.
Here is one little duck.
Go in, little duck.

The ducks see me.
The ducks swim to me.
Here is the mother duck.
Here come the little ducks.
Come to me, little ducks.

On the Swing

Here is a swing.
We can go on it.
Come and swing, Mark.
I like to swing.

14

Here I go, Mark.
Here I go up.
Here I go down.
See me go up and down.
I like to go on swings.
Swings go up and down.

I like this swing.
Two can go on it.
Here we go, Kathy.
We go up and down.
It is a good swing.

Mark

Come and see this, Kathy.
This is a good toy.
See it go up.
It can go up and up.
I like this toy.

See it come down.
Here it comes.
I can jump up to it.
Down it comes.
Down, down.

This is a good toy.
It is a rocket.
A rocket can go up.
Come here, Socks.
See the rocket go up.

Look at this, Kathy.
I like this.
It is good.
Come and look, Socks.
Look at this.

Look at me, Kathy.
See me run and jump.
I can go up in a rocket.
I can go up and up.

The House

Come in, Mark.
This is a good little house.
Come and see it.
We can play here.
I like to play in it.

We can play house.
Come and see, Mark.
Look at this.
Here is the tea.
We can have tea.
I like tea.

Here is Socks.
Socks can have tea.
Come in, Socks.
Come and have this.
Jump up, jump up.

The Train Ride

Look, Kathy, look.
Look at the little train.
I want to ride in it.
Come on, Kathy.
Come and ride.

Here comes Daddy.
Look, Daddy.
Look at the little train.
We want to ride in it.
It is a good train.

Here, Mark.
You can have a ride.
Here, Kathy.
You can have a ride.
You can have one ride.
Have a good ride.

Come on, Kathy.
Jump on the train.
I want a ride.
You want a ride.
Jump on.
This train wants to go.

Look, Mark.
I can not see Daddy.
Can you?
I like this train.
I like to ride in it.
I want two rides.

Ann

Ann, Ann.
I want you.
Come and play.
Come to my house.
We can skip.

34

Mother, Mother.
Can I go and play?
Kathy wants me.
We want to skip.

I can come, Kathy.
Look up the street.
Look down the street.
I can not see a car.
No, not one.
Here I come.

Come on, Ann.
We can skip here.
You can skip with me.
One, two, three.
Skip with me.

Look out, Ann.
Look out.
Here comes Mark.
No, Mark, no.
Mother, Mother.
Look at Mark.

Look out, Kathy.
Here we go.
Come on, Socks.
We do not want to skip.
You two can skip.
We want to go.

One, two.
I see you.
I can skip.
Can you? Can you?

One, two, three.
Come and see.
I skip with Ann.
Ann skips with me.